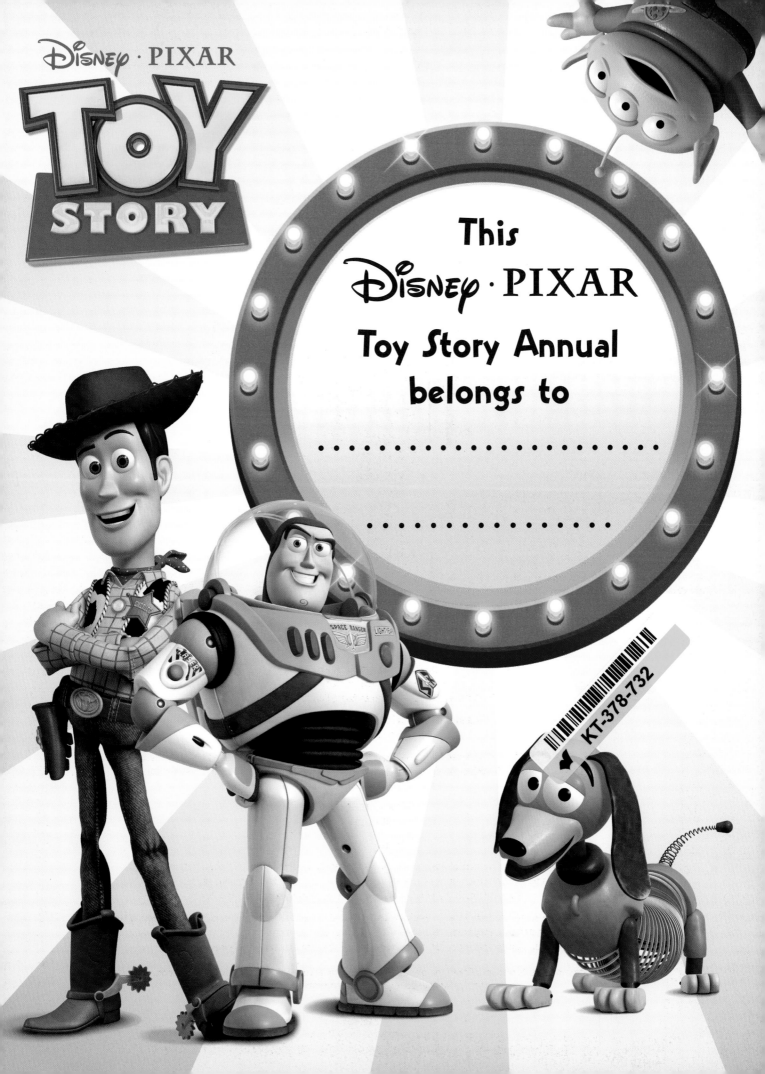

Disney · PIXAR

TOY STORY

This

Disney · PIXAR

Toy Story Annual
belongs to

....

....

KT-378-732

CONTENTS

EGMONT
We bring stories to life

First published in Great Britain in 2019
by Egmont UK Limited,
The Yellow Building, 1 Nicholas Road, London W11 4AN

Written and adapted by Helen Archer and Jude Exley
Designed by Claire Yeo

ISBN 978 1 4052 9425 6
70375/004

Printed in Italy

TURN THE PAGE AND LET THE ADVENTURES BEGIN ...

MEET THE GANG

Meet Woody, Buzz, Jessie, Dolly, Rex and Trixie. They're some of Bonnie's favourite toys and they love to play together.

WOODY

TOP TOY FACTS

TOY TYPE:

Cowboy pull-string doll

SPECIAL TALENTS:

Natural leader and good friend

MOST FAMOUS QUOTE:

You're my favourite deputy!

BEST FRIENDS:

The whole gang!

TOP SECRET!

Did you know that Woody is VERY ticklish?

JESSIE

TOP TOY FACTS

TOY TYPE:

Cowgirl doll

SPECIAL TALENTS:

Riding Bullseye and yodelling

MOST FAMOUS QUOTE:

Say that again!

BEST FRIENDS:

Woody, Bullseye and Buzz

WONDERFUL WOODY:

Sheriff Woody is a natural leader. The clever cowboy takes control in stressful situations and the other toys trust him – well, most of the time!

BUZZ

TOP TOY FACTS

TOY TYPE:
Space Ranger action figure

SPECIAL TALENTS:
Flying and saving galaxies

MOST FAMOUS QUOTE:
To infinity ... and beyond!

BEST FRIEND:
Sheriff Woody!

Buzz is a true hero. Rescuing the fearless cowgirl, Jessie, is a top priority for him!

DOLLY

Woody and Dolly are both leaders amongst their fellow toys! Woody has always been head of the gang from Andy's room, while Bonnie's toys look up to the smart and sassy Dolly.

TOP DOLL:
One of the most quick-witted and outgoing of Bonnie's toys, Dolly is a natural at taking the lead when meeting new people!

REX

TOP TOY FACTS

TOY TYPE:
Large, green Tyrannosaurus Rex

SPECIAL TALENTS:
Working a remote control with his foot; using his pointy tail to rescue the toys

MOST FAMOUS QUOTE:
Should we be HYSTERICAL?!

BEST FRIENDS:
Trixie, Woody and Buzz

MR. POTATO HEAD

FACTS

NAME: Mr. Potato Head

HE'S COOL BECAUSE:
He's a hero! He can attach his body parts to anything

BEST TOY STORY MOMENT:
Trying to escape Sunnyside using a flour tortilla

WORST TOY STORY MOMENT: Having his tortilla body pecked by a pigeon!

WE'RE TWO OF A KIND.

TRIXIE

TOP TOY FACTS

TOY TYPE:
Triceratops made of hard-wearing plastic

SPECIAL TALENTS:
Playing videogames

MOST FAMOUS QUOTE:
... that's nothing, let's just take care of that. It's just a dinosaur!

BEST FRIENDS:
Rex, Buttercup, Dolly, Mr. Pricklepants, Chuckles and the Peas-in-a-Pod

MRS. POTATO HEAD

FACTS

NAME: Mrs. Potato Head

SHE'S COOL BECAUSE: Her eye spies on what's going on ... everywhere!

BEST TOY STORY MOMENT: Meeting the Aliens. She just loves them!

WORST TOY STORY MOMENT: When Mr. Potato Head is locked up by Big Baby

OH, MY SWEET POTATO!

11

DIFFERENT FRIENDS

There are five differences between these two pictures of Woody, Buzz and Jessie. Can you spot them all?

1

2

MISSING TOY!

Each of these toys must appear only once in every row and column. Draw each missing toy, or write its name, in the correct empty square.

Rex   Woody   Buzz   Jessie

COWBOY COLOURING

Woody wants to play. Draw your own cowboy scene behind Woody and colour his picture, so he can get started.

LET'S PLAY!

MISSION ACCOMPLISHED!
COLOUR WHEN FINISHED.

MATCHING FRIENDS

Draw a line to match each character to their black-and-white version, then colour them in!

MISSION ACCOMPLISHED!

COLOUR WHEN FINISHED.

15

THE STORY SO FAR

Woody, Buzz and Jessie have come a long way since we first met them. They still live with their best friends Rex, Bullseye, Hamm, Slinky and the rest of the gang. But they have loads of new friends like Dolly and Buttercup too. Best of all, they have a new child to play with them, Bonnie!

When Bonnie met the toys at Sunnyside Daycare, she was kind to them all and they helped her become more confident. Bonnie and the toys were thrilled when Andy dropped them off at her house on his way to college.

Now Bonnie plays with Woody and the gang every day. They build spaceships which Buzz pilots, defeat the evil witch, Dolly, and have tea parties with Mr. Pricklepants. But don't worry, the toys still get up to some adventures on their own. Rex and Trixie can often be found playing their favourite computer game – if only Rex's arms were a little longer so that he could press all the keys! It's a good thing he has Trixie there to help him.

Then when Bonnie goes to daycare she has all of Woody's other friends to play with like Barbie, Ken and Baby. They send Woody and the gang letters hidden in Bonnie's backpack so that the friends can always stay in touch. Ken and Barbie even stowed away in the backpack once hoping to be taken on Bonnie's family trip to Hawaii!

Woody and the gang are back to being toys that get played with and best of all they've got lots of new friends to play with too.

MEET BONNIE'S TOYS

Say a big 'Howdy!' to all the toys Woody makes friends with at Bonnie's house.

BUTTERCUP
Buttercup is a sparkly unicorn with a deep, gruff voice!

TRIXIE
This Triceratops is friendly and loves playing on the computer.

BONNIE
This little girl loves making up new games with Woody and her other toys. Her mum works at Sunnyside Daycare.

Colour in the picture

DOLLY
Dolly is a cute ragdoll. She likes to be the leader of Bonnie's toys.

MR. PRICKLEPANTS
This soft but spiky hedgehog is a bit of a show-off. He loves getting the main part in Bonnie's games.

CHUCKLES
This clown doesn't look too happy. That's because his first owner lost him.

PEAS-IN-A-POD
These three peas are like brothers and sisters. They live together in a zip-up-pod.

Can you spot these items in the big picture?
Tick the boxes as you find them.

PUZZLE TIME!

Here are some great puzzles for you, so get your pencil out!

1

GUESS WHO?
Match the right shadow to the right character.

1

2

3

A

B

C

PUZZLE YOUR WAY AROUND THESE TRICKY CHALLENGES!

MISSION ACCOMPLISHED!
COLOUR WHEN FINISHED.

Answer: 1. 1 - B, 2 - A, 3 - C; 2. The parts belong to Mr. Pricklepants; 3. Hamm is missing from picture B.

2 PUZZLING PARTS
Can you work out who all these parts belong to? Tick the correct box.

3 WHO'S MISSING?
Can you spot who is missing from picture B?

A

B

BALLOON MISSION!

Buttercup, Dolly and Mr. Pricklepants have all got a balloon. Follow the strings to find out what colour balloon each toy is holding.

TEA TIME FUN!

The toys are having a tea party today.
Do these activities to join in the delicious fun!

Draw a cake with icing and berries to make the tea table complete.

2

1

4

3

5

Finish off the picture by matching the stars to the correct blank spaces. Now the toys can tuck in!

B

D

A 3

C

E

23

MEET THE NEW TOYS

There are a lot of new toys to meet in Toy Story 4, but some of them are friendlier than others.

OFFICER GIGGLE MCDIMPLES is a tiny police officer with a tiny car and house to match. She is excited to meet Sheriff Woody and as the Pet Patrol Officer, she's the perfect member of the Forky rescue team.

GABBY GABBY is a doll from the 1950s who lives in the antique shop. All she really wants is to be loved by the owner's granddaughter, Harmony, and she'll do anything to make that happen.

FORKY is Bonnie's art project and her favourite toy. He is made out of a plastic spork, pipe cleaners and googly eyes, but he doesn't realise how important he is to Bonnie and instead hides in the bin where he feels safest.

DUKE CABOOM is a stunt toy from the 1970s who spends his days inside a vintage pinball machine at the antique shop. It's the one place where the toys can relax away from Gabby Gabby's control.

DUCKY AND BUNNY were carnival prizes who hung from a booth, waiting to be won. They are attached at the hand and wish they weren't always together, but their teamwork proves invaluable.

DUCKY AND BUNNY'S ESCAPE

Ducky and Bunny are trying to help Buzz escape the funfair stall but there are three different paths for them to take. Which path leads them to the exit?

1 2 3

EXIT

GABBY GABBY'S TEA PARTY

Forky is having tea with Gabby Gabby.
Colour in the picture of their tea party.

PART ONE

Disney · PIXAR
TOY STORY 4

Bonnie loved playing with Woody and the gang, but as time went on, Woody found himself being played with less and less. Then one day, Woody heard that Bonnie was going to kindergarten. She was nervous and didn't want to go, so Woody jumped into her backpack to keep an eye on her.

In the classroom, a boy accidentally threw Bonnie's art supplies away. Woody sneaked to the bin and took out a spork, a pipe cleaner and some googly eyes. Bonnie used these to make Forky! At the end of orientation, Bonnie put Forky into her backpack, right next to Woody. Then Forky came to life!

Back in Bonnie's room, Woody introduced Forky to the toys and explained that he was important to Bonnie. "We all have to make sure nothing happens to him." But Woody soon discovered that it wasn't easy to take care of Forky, as he would constantly run to the bin. That night, when Woody brought him back to Bonnie, she pulled Woody into her arms, too.

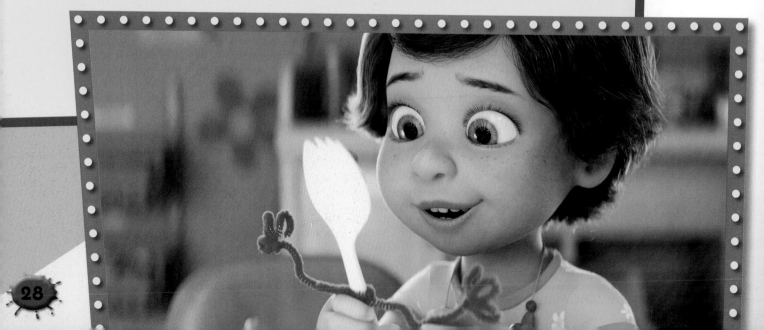

Bonnie's family decided to take a road trip before the start of school. But at every stop, Woody had to keep bringing Forky back from the bin. Then, without warning, Forky jumped out of the moving RV crying, "I am not a toy, I'm a spork!"

Woody quickly climbed through the window and found Forky by the side of the road. "Like it or not, you are a toy," said Woody. "And you have to be there for Bonnie." Forky realised that she loved him the same way he loved trash and she needed him.

Just before morning, the toys passed a store called Second Chance Antiques where Woody saw Bo Peep's lamp in the window. Woody missed Bo and wanted to see if she was in the store, so he wriggled through the letter box with Forky. There they met a doll called Gabby Gabby who told them she'd take them to Bo. But she really wanted Woody's voice box as hers was broken. Suddenly they were surrounded by dolls who snatched Forky! Then Harmony, the shop owner's granddaughter, picked up Woody and took him to the park, leaving Forky behind.

Back in the RV, Bonnie realised that Forky was missing.
"Mum! Dad! I can't find Forky," she cried.
Bonnie and her parents looked everywhere. Buzz decided to jump out the window to look for Forky and Woody. He soon ended up in the carnival where he was picked up and put on a game booth as a prize!

Meanwhile, Woody had escaped from Harmony and he'd found Bo Peep! Bo told Woody she'd been a lost toy for seven years. One of her closest friends was a tiny police officer called Giggle McDimples. Woody asked them for help to rescue Forky, but Bo shrugged. "Kids lose toys every day. Bonnie will get over it." Then Woody reminded her about how she had once been a child's favourite toy. Bo smiled and agreed to help rescue Forky. Everyone piled into Bo's car, called the skunkmobile since it looked so much like a skunk, and they zoomed away.

At the carnival, Buzz struggled to free himself from the prize wall. But in his attempts, he freed two other toys, Ducky and Bunny too. They were furious with Buzz. "Put us back up there right now!" yelled Bunny. But Buzz was already on the move.

Nearby, the skunkmobile weaved its way through the crowd. Bo had an idea. They could get to the antiques store by jumping along the tops of the game booths. As they climbed the carousel, Woody asked Bo how she'd become a lost toy. "My kid grew up and didn't need me anymore," said Bo. "Who needs a kid's room when you can have all of this?" she asked. She would be leaving with the carnival in the morning.

Back at the RV, Bonnie's family was ready to leave. Woody, Buzz, and Forky would be left behind! The toys didn't know what to do, but Jessie had an idea. She jumped out of the window and the gang heard a loud POP! "We're not going anywhere," smiled Jessie — she had burst the tyre!

Just as the Ferris wheel reached the top and the friends jumped out, Buzz spotted Woody. He climbed up to meet him and was surprised to see Bo! Suddenly, Ducky and Bunny tackled Buzz. They were angry, but Woody promised they could come to Bonnie's room if they helped rescue Forky. The toys leaped down the airshaft into the store.

CONTINUED ON PAGE 50

PICTURE PERFECT

Bonnie has been taking photos of Buzz, Woody and Jessie.
Can you count how many pictures she has taken of each character?

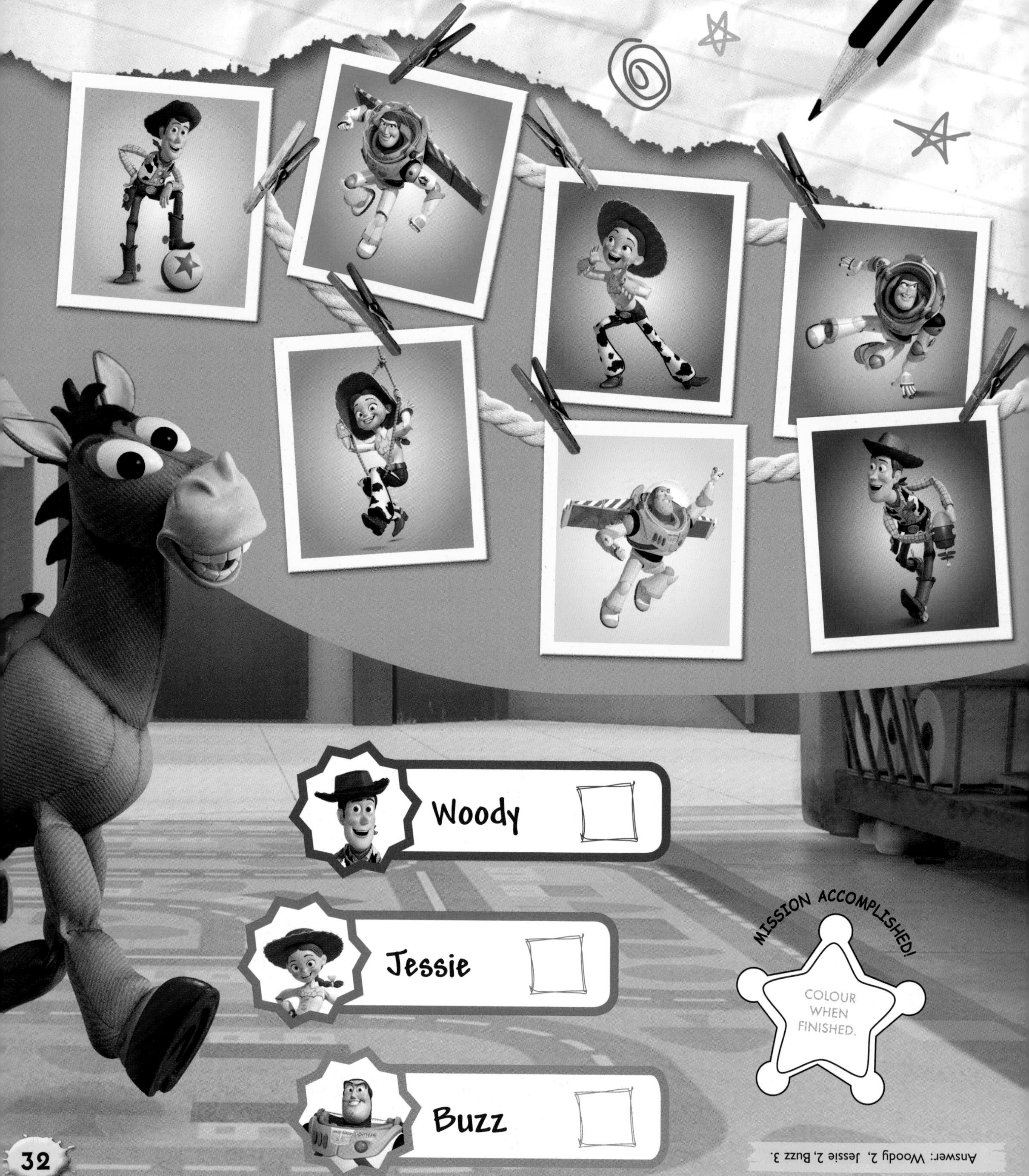

Woody ☐

Jessie ☐

Buzz ☐

MISSION ACCOMPLISHED!

COLOUR WHEN FINISHED.

32

HOWDY PARTNER

Use your colours to get Buzz and Woody ready for action.

33

BIG AND SMALL

Woody and Jessie have been squeezed and stretched!
Put them in the right order from the biggest to the
smallest. We've done the first one for you.

BIG

C

SMALL

A   B   C   D

BIG

D

SMALL

A   B   C   D

Answers: Woody: C, A, D, B. Jessie: D, A, B, C.

POTATO PUZZLE

Help Mrs. Potato Head find her way through the maze picking up her husband's parts on the way!

How many parts of Mr. Potato Head did you collect?

START

THAT SPUD IS SO MESSY!

FINISH

Answer: 7 parts.

Meet Bo Peep

BO PEEP is a porcelain shepherd who never goes anywhere without her sheep, Billy, Goat, and Gruff. She was Molly's toy, and is one of Woody's oldest friends, who is always there to help the toys when they are in trouble.

Since being given away by Molly, BO PEEP now lives life with her band of lost toys. They travel from playground to playground helping children to have fun but never belonging to one child.

Draw over the lines to complete the sentence.

BO PEEP is very

BRAVE.

40

MISSING SHEEP

Bo Peep's sheep are hiding in this scene.
Can you help her find them?
Circle the sheep when you do.

MISSION ACCOMPLISHED!

COLOUR WHEN FINISHED.

REX AND TRIXIE

Rex has always been worried about meeting a new dinosaur, but sweet-natured Trixie is the perfect pre-historic pal.

I'M GONNA GET PLAYED WITH!

WE'RE PRE-HISTORIC PLAYMATES!

SPLASH OF COLOUR

Colour this picture of Dolly and the Peas-in-a-Pod.

Use the numbers and the colour splats to help you colour this picture.

How many different colour splats are there on this page?

Answer: There are eight colour splats.

ODD TOY OUT

Look carefully at these three photos.
Can you find the odd toy out in each one?

STRANGE THINGS ARE HAPPENING HERE!

1

a

c

b

2

a

b

c

3

a

b

c

d

MISSION ACCOMPLISHED!

COLOUR WHEN FINISHED.

Answers: 1 - b, 2 - b, 3 - d.

HAT HUNT

Draw a lasso round Woody's real hat so that he can prove he's a cowboy.

what does woody's hat look like?

it's wide...

...and brown all over.

a

b

c

d

e

f

Design a new hat for Woody in the space below.

WHO'S NEXT?

Help Andy work out which toys are missing in the sequence.

Shout out or draw the missing friends!

1

2

3

OPERATION PLAYTIME

Woody wants to make sure that all the toys in the toy box get played with. Solve these teasers and let playtime begin ...

1 COUNTING FUN

The peas have got some more friends for their pod. Help Woody round them up by counting how many there are.

2 TINY TOYS

Can you put the family of Troikas in height order, starting with the shortest first?

A   B   C   D   E

The correct order is:

D _ _ _ _ _

3

SPELL IT OUT

Help Mr. Spell unscramble the letters to reveal a mystery word. We have entered some of the letters for you.

LPAYTEIM

P _ _ A _ T _ M _

4

WHO'S THAT?

Jessie is looking for one of her friends. Can you work out who it is from these close-ups?

B _ _ _ _ _ _ _

MISSION ACCOMPLISHED!

COLOUR WHEN FINISHED.

Answers: 1) There are 5 peas, 2) D, A, B, C, E, 3) PLAYTIME, 4) Bullseye.

49

PART TWO

Disney · PIXAR

TOY STORY 4

Forky was in Gabby Gabby's glass cabinet, but first they'd need to avoid Dragon, the store's cat. Bo had a plan. She took Woody to a secret hangout inside an old pinball machine. Bo wanted Duke Caboom, the stuntman toy, to jump across the aisle to rescue her sheep and Forky. But Duke was worried he couldn't do it.

"Be the Duke you are right now," said Bo and Duke knew he could help.
"You've handled this lost toy life better than I could," Woody told Bo. "You have a way of making a toy see the best in themselves."

Finally, the mission was underway. With a yarn tied to his belt, Woody was on the bike behind Duke. The stuntman sped off, but he began to panic – Duke was going down! Woody jumped off the bike and grabbed the cabinet knob as Duke crashed next to Dragon. Bo used the yarn to zip across to the cabinet and get Forky! But Gabby Gabby held on to Woody's pullstring, so he landed back in the cabinet, and Forky fell to the floor. Woody swung down to get him and landed on the cat!

In the meantime, Bo told everyone to grab onto the yarn. Duke zoomed past Dragon, who chased him through the store into the alley. But Forky had been left behind. Woody returned to the store and it didn't take long for him to find Gabby Gabby. "I'd give anything to be loved the way you have," she said. Woody knew what he had to do. "Just leave me Forky. Bonnie needs him," he replied, giving her his voice box.

Meanwhile, Buzz had returned to the RV. He had seen Bonnie's backpack in the antique store and he needed her to go back. But Bonnie's dad had just fixed the tyre and was about to leave. "Your backpack's in the antique store. Let's go!" he blurted out. Bonnie suddenly remembered and asked her parents to return to the store.

Back in the shop, Gabby Gabby was delighted with her new voice box. But Harmony thought she was creepy and she tossed Gabby Gabby aside. Woody and Forky were shocked, but there was no time to wait—they heard Bonnie enter the store. Woody grabbed Forky and jumped into the backpack. Moments later, Bonnie picked up her backpack and found Forky inside. She was thrilled!

On the way out of the store, Woody made a decision. "Tell Buzz to get the RV to the merry-go-round," he said to Forky. Then he jumped out of the backpack and returned to Gabby Gabby, who said "You can have your voice box. I don't need it anymore." Woody told Gabby Gabby that Harmony wasn't her only chance at getting a kid—he would take her to Bonnie! Bo overheard Woody and wanted to help Gabby Gabby, too. "C'mon, let's get you to Bonnie," she said and they headed off.

At the carnival, Bo and Woody persuaded Duke to do his next daredevil stunt, by jumping across the carnival. "I am Duke CA-BOOM! I can do this!" cried Duke, as he launched himself off the Ferris wheel, sailing over the carnival with ease. All memories of his past failures faded away as he crashed his bike right on target.

The toys zipped across the string of flags that Duke had pulled behind him. As they approached the carousel, Gabby Gabby saw a girl who was lost and all alone. When the lost girl saw Gabby Gabby she hugged her and worked up the courage to ask a security guard for help. She carried her new doll as she looked for her parents. Gabby Gabby finally had a kid.

Meanwhile, Bonnie's toys had got the RV to the carnival. Bonnie's dad had started to drive a different way, so Trixie had done her best imitation of the GPS system to direct him there! Everyone was happy to see Woody and Bo, and Woody was even happier to see Bonnie reunited with Forky. He had done the job he'd set out to do. It was then he realised that there were kids and toys everywhere who would always need his help.

Woody and his friends invented a new way to find homes for lost carnival toys. They rigged the games so that the kids would win and take a toy home every time. Bo called it "Operation Toy Donation." The friends were so good at it that they gave away all the toys! Woody loved seeing kids playing with toys and toys finding happiness with kids. And he knew that wherever he went and whichever toy he helped next, he would always have his friends by his side.

THE END

QUESTION TIME

Can you answer these questions about the story?

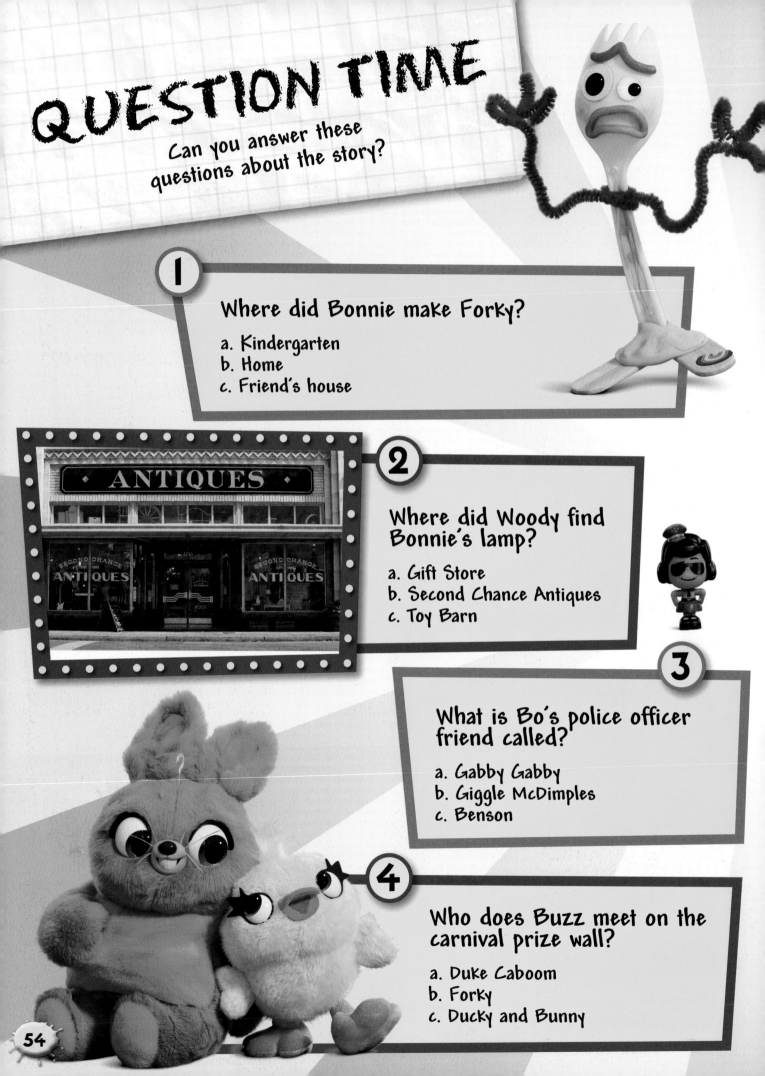

1

Where did Bonnie make Forky?

a. Kindergarten
b. Home
c. Friend's house

ANTIQUES

SECOND CHANCE ANTIQUES   SECOND CHANCE ANTIQUES

2

Where did Woody find Bonnie's lamp?

a. Gift Store
b. Second Chance Antiques
c. Toy Barn

3

What is Bo's police officer friend called?

a. Gabby Gabby
b. Giggle McDimples
c. Benson

4

Who does Buzz meet on the carnival prize wall?

a. Duke Caboom
b. Forky
c. Ducky and Bunny

54

5 Who popped the RV's tyre to stop Bonnie's family leaving?

a. Rex
b. Jessie
c. Buttercup

6 What is the stuntman toy called?

a. Rejean
b. Dragon
c. Duke Caboom

7 Who wants Woody's voice box?

a. Gabby Gabby
b. Harmony
c. Forky

8 What is the store cat called?

a. Duke
b. Dragon
c. Benson

9 Who pretended to be a GPS system to get Bonnie to the carnival?

a. Jessie
b. Dolly
c. Trixie

10 What does Bo call their plan to find homes for lost carnival toys?

a. Carnival Crew
b. Operation Toy Donation
c. Friend Finder

Answers: 1) a. 2) b. 3) b. 4) c. 5) b. 6) c. 7) a. 8) b. 9) b. 10) b.

55

COWBOY PUZZLE

Finish this picture of Woody by drawing lines to match the jigsaw pieces to the spaces.

Which image doesn't belong here?

Answers: 1 - C, 2 - A, 3 - D, 4 - B. Piece 5 doesn't belong.

BUZZ TWINS

Buzz Lightyear is the coolest space ranger!
Can you find the smaller Buzz that
matches the big picture?

a

b

c

Find Mini Buzz and
COLOUR him in.

d

e

MISSION ACCOMPLISHED!

COLOUR
WHEN
FINISHED.

THE POTATO HEADS AND THE ALIENS

Mr. and Mrs. Potato Head are a perfect match, but the family wouldn't be complete without their three adopted children. Even if those children are Aliens!

Mr. Potato Head saves the Aliens during a crazy car chase in Toy Story 2. And Mrs. Potato Head wants to adopt them!

MY SWEET POTATO!

MY HERO!

Before Mr. Potato Head met his sweet potato, he and Hamm regularly enjoyed a game of poker!

COLOUR IN

The grateful Aliens rescue their foster parents along with the rest of the toys from the fiery incinerator!

WE ARE ETERNALLY GRATEFUL!

RESCUE WOODY

Woody has been kidnapped by Al, and Buzz and the gang have set out to find him. Play the rescue game with a friend and see who is the first to save Woody.

Use a counter to move along the board. Take turns rolling a dice and move the counter as many spaces as the number you throw. If you land on a space with a picture on it, follow the instructions in the key.

How many soldiers are hiding in the grass? Colour them in.

READY GANG? LET'S GO!

START

FINISH

ER, GUYS! I'M IN THE BUILDING ACROSS FROM AL'S TOY BARN!

AL'S TOY B...

KEY

You meet Bullseye and he gives you a ride. Move forward 1 space!

You stumble upon a ball, and have to stay and play. Skip your turn!

There are roadworks ahead, and you must find another route. Move back 1 space!

61

SEEING DOUBLE

Duke Caboom is the best motorbike stuntman ever! Draw lines to match his daring stunts. Circle the one that doesn't match.

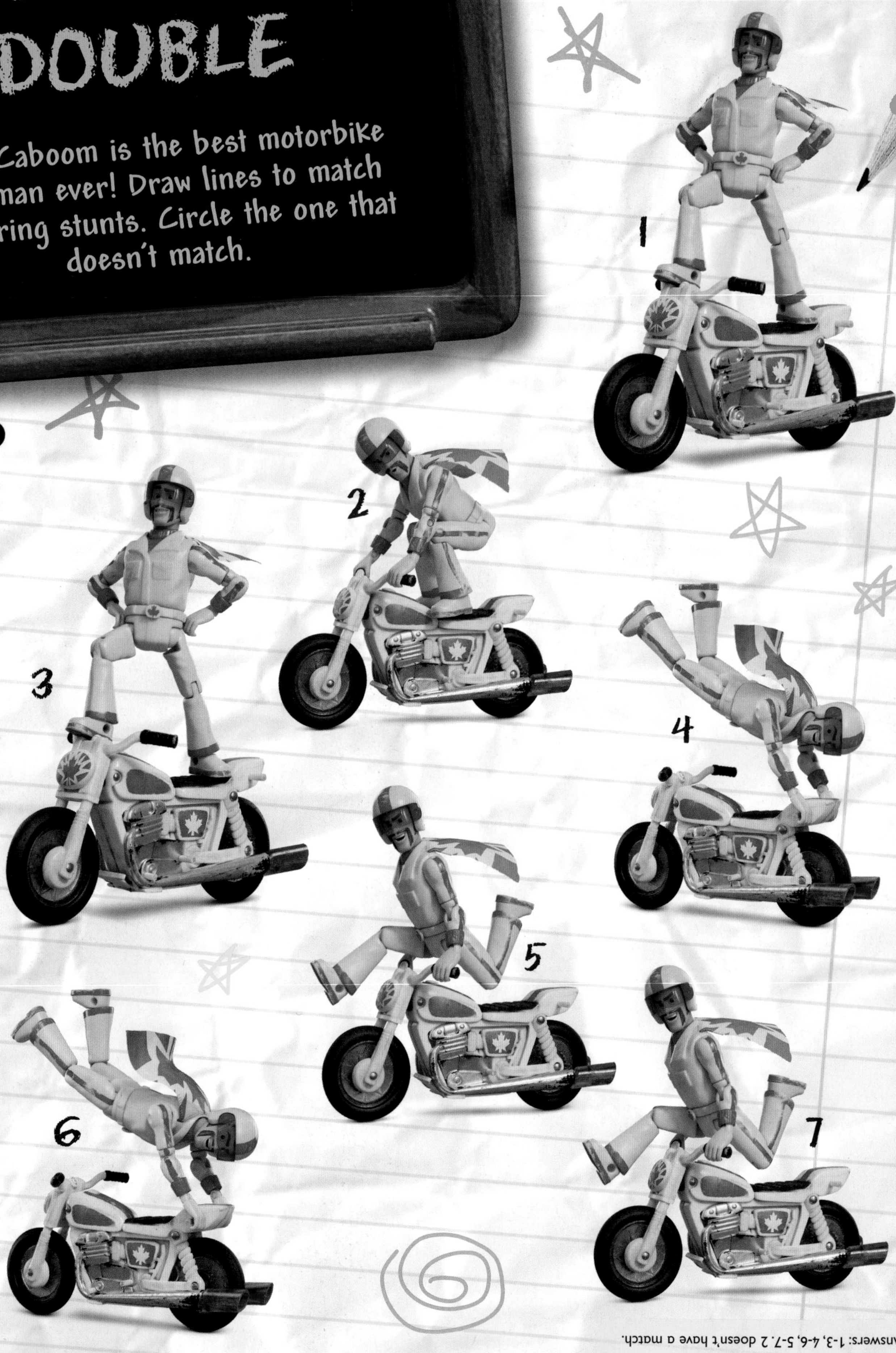

1

2

3

4

5

6

7

BONNIE'S TOYS

Bonnie's mum has taken lots of pictures of her toys, but they've come out blurry. Can you help Bonnie work out which pictures are of Bo Beep?

a

b

c

d

e

f

TOY DETECTIVE

Mr. Potato Head wants to be a detective. Follow the clues to help him find the right toy.

The toy is not GREEN

The toy is not PURPLE

colour

The toy walks on **4** legs.

The toy says NEEIIIGH!

Answer: It's Bullseye.

HIDE OUT

Buzz and Jessie are hiding some of their friends. Can you see who's behind them?

Tick each toy as you find it. Who isn't hiding?

Answer: Woody isn't hiding.

MISSION ACCOMPLISHED!

COLOUR WHEN FINISHED.

65

GOODBYE!